CW00863277

For Ron

Oxford University Press, Great Clarendon Street, Oxford OX2 6DP

Oxford is a trade mark of Oxford University Press

Text copyright © Stephen Tucker 1999
Illustrations copyright © Nick Sharratt 1999
First published 1999

A CIP catalogue record for this book is available from the British Library

ISBN 019 279028 5 (hardback)
ISBN 019 272352 9 (paperback)

Printed in Hong Kong

My Friends

by Nick Sharratt & Stephen Tucker

Oxford University Press

We've brought bread
for the ducks to eat,
They all say thank you
for their treat.
Quack! Quack! Quack!

The tiny baby's fast asleep,
tucked up in her cot.
If we go and wake her up
she'll cry, so better not.
Shhhh!

This dog is friendly,
Very big, too.
It's going to lick me!
What shall I do?

I thought I'd call to say 'Hello.'

Bye-bye for now, I've got to go.

How many fishes in the tank,
Are there three or four?
It's hard to count when
they swim about,
That's why I'm not sure.

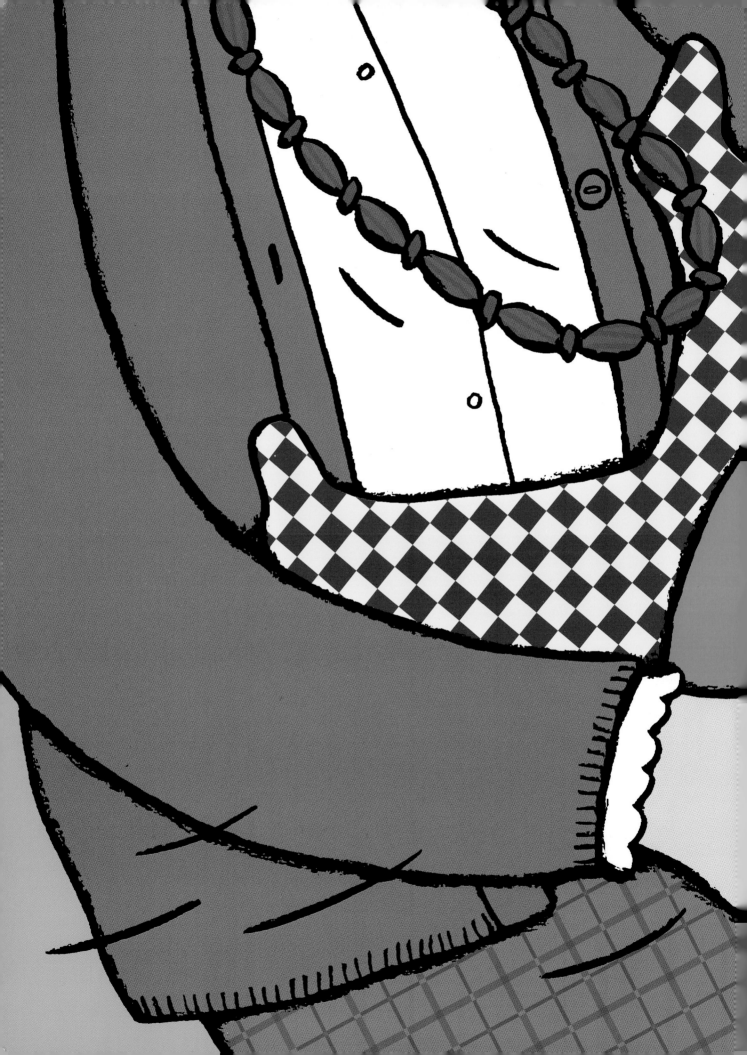

Lift me off the ground
And whirl me round
and round!

Say goodnight to Rabbit,
Say goodnight to Ted,
Say goodnight to Woolly Lamb
And snuggle down in bed.